a shabby dog story

Xpresso Books

a division of Fleetway Publications, Greater London House, Hampstead Road, London NW1 7QQ, a member

of Maxwell Consumer Publishing & Communications Ltd. UK Distribution and Export by MacDonald & Co

(Publishers) Ltd, Tel (071) 377 4600.

Steve Edgell

Editor

Frieda Leia Jacobowitz

Kim Thompson

Translation

Rian Hughes

Cover Design

Michael W Bennent

Group Editor

First published in Belgium as Le Chien Debout © 1981 Casterman

Translation © 1989 Cha Cha Comics

UK edition © 1991 Xpresso Books

ISBN 1 85386 260 6

Printed and bound in the EEC

First edition July 1991

1 3 5 7 9 10 8 6 4 2

a shabby dog story

LET'S SEE... FREDDO'S BAR WAS OVER BEHIND FATHER JULES'S SHED... A SHACK PROPPED UP AGAINST THE CHICKEN COOP...

AND STAY OUT, YA LITTLE YERK!

GAD! LOOKS LIKE IT'S STILL A SWINGING JOINT... HEH, HEH, HEH!

YOU OKAY, BUDDY?

SURE, STRANGER. I'VE BEEN WORSE.

FREDDO'S BAR

... KARTLER, THE CUSTOMS OFFICER'S FAT MUTT... THINKS HE CAN GET AWAY WITH ANYTHING 'CAUSE HIS OWNER WEARS STRIPED PANTS AND A HAT WITH STARS ON IT!

ANYWAY, GILBERTE WILL NEVER BE HIS! NEVER! HA HA HA HA!

WHAT?! Y-YOU KNOW WHERE SHE IS? TELL ME, FOR GOD'S SAKE!

SHE'S BETTER OFF WHERE SHE IS NOW, GILBERTE... AND IT AIN'T NONE OF MY BUSINESS. SEE YA, STRANGER.

BUT..?

STRANGE BIRD... WONDER WHAT HE MEANT?

DO'S BA

... AND THE FIRST ONE'A YOU PUSSIES WHO SAYS ANYTHING GETS THE SAME TREATMENT!

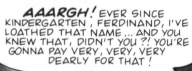

13

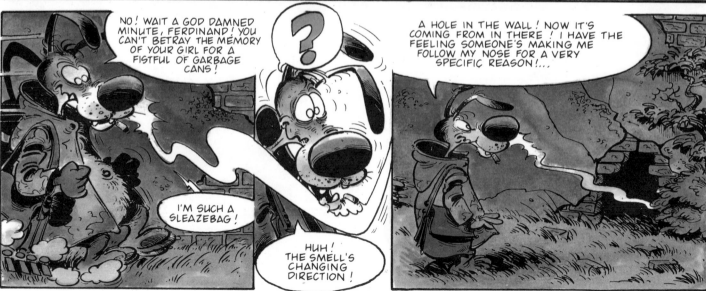

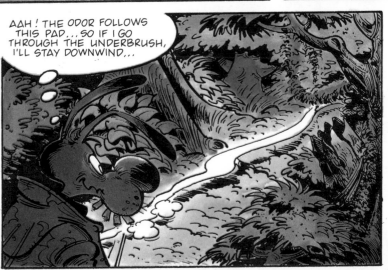

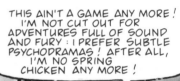

24

25

THE WAITRESS FROM THE BAR! SPUNKY LITTLE THING! THAT SCUMBAG KARTLER MUST'VE FORCED HER TO BE ONE OF HIS BITCHES DURING THE GARBAGE CAN RITUAL... POOR GIRL!

I'LL HELP YOU, TRUST ME...

HEY YOU! GIDDADA HERE! NO ONE TALKS TO THE PRISONER!

EGZELLUNT! SCHPLENDID!

?

PURR-FECT, KARTLER! VELL DONE! VERY VELL DONE! GUT! GUT!

HOLY GOD! SO THIS IS THE TERRIBLE DOCTOR CALHOUN!

ACH! GUT DOGGIE, GUT PUPPY!

HA! HA! WHO LOOKS LIKE AN ASSHOLE NOW?

ACH! MINE DEAR IRRENA, ZE PRROPENSITY ZAT ZIS DOG DISPLAYS TO BETRRAY HIS OWN KIND NEFFER CEASES TO AMAZE ME!

GET A LOAD OF THAT! HIS MASTER'S VOICE, HUH?

IFF ZIS ANIMAL VOSS NOT INDISPENSABLE FOR ZE PURRPOSE UFF ENTRRAPPING HISS FELLOW CANINES, I'D LIKE TO EGGSAMINE HISS CORTEX!

GLUP

UND NOW, DEAR IRRENA, YOU MUST BRRING ALL ZOSE DOGS TO ZE LABORATORY! I SHALL BEGIN MIT DER TRREAT-MENT IMMEDIATELY!

GUT, HERR DOCTOR!

?

OH, JESUS! I'VE GOTTA BE DREAMING!

SO THAT'S HOW ALL THE SUCKERS END UP WHO WERE ATTRACTED BY THE SMELL OF GARBAGE: GUINEA PIGS FOR THE EXPERIMENTS OF AN INSANE SCIENTIST!

THE ONLY REASON I'M NOT LINED UP WITH THOSE OTHER POOR BASTARDS IS BECAUSE I WAS OUT COLD. BUT I SHOULDN'T KID MYSELF: I'LL BE NEXT!

OF COURSE, KARTLER'S GOONS AND THE CAT IN THE WOODS ALSO HAD THOSE WIRES IN THEIR SKULLS. THAT MEANS THEY CAME THROUGH HERE... AND GOT OUT ALIVE... BUT THAT AIN'T MUCH OF A HOPE: THEY ALL LOOKED TOTALLY WASTED...

AND WITH THOSE WORDS, OUR HERO COURAGEOUSLY FALLS INTO A DEEP, DARK BLUE FUNK...

WHERE IN THE NAME OF CHRIST HAVE I LANDED?

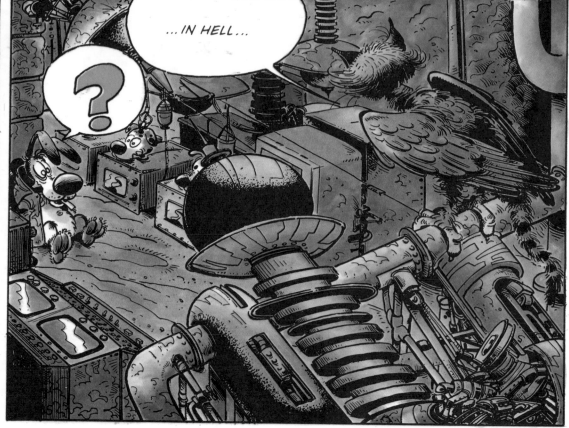

...IN HELL...

?

32

... ALL RIGHT, THEN ...

LET'S HEAR YOUR RIDDLE!

AAH!

SO TELL ME: WHAT WALKS ON FOUR LEGS MORNING, NOON, AND NIGHT?

SON OF A... THE GIRL FROM THE BAR! GUTSY CHICK!

SO! GIVE UP?

WELL... UUHH...

PAF

?

HEH, HEH! WELL DONE, HONEY!

GET ME OUTTA THIS!

OKAY, OKAY!

I'VE ALSO GOT YOUR BAG, MR. FERDINAND, WITH YOUR GUN AND AMMO!

CLICK!

HA-AAAH! JUST WHAT THE DOCTOR ORDERED, HEH HEH!

WE'VE GOT TO HURRY! THE DOCTOR COULD COME BACK AT ANY MOMENT!

NO! WAIT!

WHAT ABOUT THEM? WE CAN'T LEAVE THEM LIKE THAT!

BESIDES, I STILL DON'T KNOW WHO KILLED GILBERTE! YOU'VE GOTTA TELL ME!

LISTEN, MR. FERDINAND, DON'T YOU THINK YOU'VE STARED DEATH IN THE FACE ENOUGH TIMES FOR ONE DAY?

PLEASE! LET'S LEAVE NOW!

NO! THIS STORY'S GOT TO HAVE A HERO... OTHERWISE, WHAT'S THE POINT? HUH?

MMMM...

O.K.... I'LL TELL YOU EVERYTHING...

IT ALL STARTED A YEAR AGO, WHEN THE DOCTOR MOVED IN...

THIS SECLUDED HOUSE FIT HIS DASTARDLY PLANS TO A "T"...

ACH! TEUFEL! GUT, GUT!

HE BUILT A LABORATORY AND THREW HIMSELF IMMEDIATELY INTO HIS HORRIBLE EXPERIMENTS...

IN THE BEGINNING, HE CAPTURED STRAY DOGS THAT ROAMED ON THE FIELDS...

YIP!

GUT! GUT!

35

BECAUSE HIS VICTIMS' HORRIBLE SHRIEKS OF PAIN ANNOYED HIM, THE DOCTOR REGULARY GAVE THEM HEFTY DOSES OF MORPHINE...

BUT A FEW HIDEOUSLY MAIMED DOGS ESCAPED ... IN THE THROES OF WITHDRAWAL, THEY FRANTICALLY SEARCHED EVERYWHERE FOR THE DRUG WITHOUT WHICH THEY COULD NO LONGER LIVE...

THE ONLY ONE WHO COULD PROCURE IT FOR THEM WAS *KARTLER*, THE CUSTOMS OFFICER'S DOG... AND *GILBERTE'S* LOVER...

HIS OWNER, A PETTY OFFICIAL, CONFIS-CATED DRUGS ON A REGULAR BASIS FROM ALL KINDS OF DEALERS WHO TRIED TO SMUGGLE IT PAST HIS BORDER POST...

LOUSY KIDS! (MUTTER...)

NOT WANTING ANY TROUBLE, HE'D BURY THE STUFF IN A VEGETABLE GARDEN, RATHER THAN INFORMING HIS SUPERIORS...

ALL *KARTLER* HAD TO DO WAS DIG IT UP AT NIGHT, HELPED BY HIS FAITHFULL ASSISTANT, *THE GELDING* !

GIMME!

WHEW!

THEY DOLED OUT THE DRUGS IN SMALL DOSES AMONG THE "VIVISECTED" DOGS, IN EXCHANGE FOR THEIR TOTAL OBEDIENCE. AND SO *KARTLER* BUILT UP A REGULAR ARMY, READY TO DO ANYTHING FOR HIM !

YE...YESS !

NEXT !

KARTLER HAD BECOME THE UNCONTESTED RULER OF THE REGION, BUT HIS MEGALOMANIA KNEW NO BOUNDS... AND THE DOCTOR NEEDED STILL MORE DOGS!

THOSE TWO WERE MADE FOR EACH OTHER: THEY SET UP THE GARBAGE CAN TRAPS WITH WHICH YOU YOURSELF WERE CAPTURED.

ACH, DONNERWETTER! PERFECT !

TEUFEL !

HIMMELZACKER !

GUT! GUT !

KARTLER ASKED HIS MISTRESS *GILBERTE* TO WORK AS A BITCH FOR HIM... SHE REFUSED POINT BLANK!

41

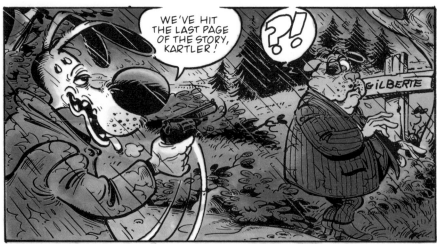

43

NOOO!

I'M SORRY TO SAY, THAT'S THE GOD'S HONEST TRUTH. ON PAGE 4, PANEL 6, YOU PITCHED AN EMPTY WINE BOTTLE INTO THE BUSHES WHERE SHE WAS HIDING... IT LANDED ON HER HEAD...

DEAD ON IMPACT!

...NOOOO!

GILBERTE DISAPPEARED AFTER SHE BROKE UP WITH WITH KARTLER. KARTLER OFFERED ME A LOT OF MONEY TO FIND HER. I NEEDED THE DOUGH, SO I TOOK ON THE JOB...

ON THE DAY YOU TURNED UP, I'D FINALLY PICKED UP HER TRAIL. SHE WAS HIDING IN THE BUSHES WHERE YOU WERE HAVING YOUR PICNIC. SHE WAS GAZING SO INTENTLY AT YOU THAT SHE DIDN'T NOTICE I'D FOLLOWED HER.

ALL OF SUDDEN, SHE RECOGNIZED YOU! SHE RUSHES FORWARD! YOUR BOTTLE COMES FLYING!

SHE DIED IN MY ARMS... I SHUT HER EYES... AND LEFT HER THERE, IN THE LUSH GRASS... HER FEET IN THE GLADIOLAS... HER LITTLE WHITE DRESS WAS SOAKED WITH BLOOD ...AND SHE SEEMED TO SMILE INTO THE RAINDROPS THAT WERE KISSING HER SWEET FACE... OR, RATHER, WHAT WAS LEFT OF IT!

GILBERTE'S DEATH WAS BAD NEWS: KARTLER MIGHT VERY WELL BLAME IT ON ME. I DIDN'T REALIZE HE'D FIND IT MORE CONVENIENT TO BLAME YOU...

SO I HIGH-TAILED IT UP TO THE VILLAGE TO DEMAND MY FEE BEFORE KARTLER GOT WIND OF THE FACT THAT HIS EX-MISTRESS WAS DEAD. I TOLD HIM THAT GILBERTE MUST HAVE LEFT THE COUNTRY AND THAT I'D STOPPED MY INVESTI-GATIONS, SINCE THEY WERE NOW POINTLESS,

KARTLER WAS BESIDE HIMSELF! HE HAD ME THROWN OUT LIKE A BUM! JUST AT THAT MOMENT YOU ARRIVED...

THAT WAS WHEN I DECIDED TO SEEK REVENGE MY WAY: USING A CATSPAW,

AND I WAS TO BE THE CATSPAW?

EXACTLY! I DON'T LIKE BEING THE STAR; I'D RATHER PULL THE STRINGS FROM BEHIND THE SCENES.

YOU MUST BE PRETTY PLEASED!

NO ..... WHEN YOU KILLED *CALHOUN*, YOU WENT TOO FAR, THE DOCTOR WAS THE LEADER OF THE CULT OF CHAOS THAT REIGNED HERE.

NOW THE AREA IS OVERRUN WITH CRAZIES, SICKOS AND JUNKIES...OR STIFFS...SEE, I CAN GET ALONG PRETTY GOOD IN A CHAOS BORNE OUT OF LOGIC OR CONFLICT-ING MORALITY...BUT TOTAL ANARCHY, THAT'S SOME-THING ELSE!

YOU CAN DO WHAT YOU WANT, STRANGER, BUT I'M GONE!

XPRESSO BOOKS

Troubled Souls   *Garth Ennis and John McCrea*   UK £6.50/US $9.95

For a Few Troubles More   *Garth Ennis, John McCrea and Wendy Simpson*   UK £3.95/US $7.95

The Complete New Statesmen   *John Smith, Jim Baikie, Duncan Fegredo and Sean Phillips*   UK £7.95/US $14.95

Heart Throbs   *Max Cabanes*   UK £6.99*

2000 AD BOOKS

Anderson Psi Division: Shamballa   *Alan Grant and Arthur Ransom*   UK £4.99/US $9.95

Chopper: Song of the Surfer   *John Wagner and Colin MacNeil*   UK £5.95/US $9.95

Hewligan's Haircut   *Peter Milligan and Jamie Hewlett*   UK £4.50/US $5.95

The Judge Child Quest   *John Wagner, Alan Grant, Brian Bolland, Mike McMahon and Ron Smith*   UK £6.95/US $12.95

The Judge Dredd Mega-Collection   *John Wagner, Alan Grant and Ron Smith*   UK £6.95/US $14.95

Judge Dredd in Tale of the Dead Man   *John Wagner, Will Simpson, Wendy Simpson and Jeff Anderson*   UK £4.99/US $8.95

Sláine: The Horned God   *Pat Mills and Simon Bisley*

Volume 1 UK £4.50/US $7.95

Volume 2 UK £4.99/US $7.95

Volume 3 UK £5.95/US $7.95

DEFINITIVE EDITIONS

Judge Dredd – Bad Science   *Wagner, Grant, Mills and McMahon*   UK £4.50/US $7.95

Judge Dredd – Future Crime   *Wagner, Grant and Bolland*   £4.50/US $7.95

Judge Dredd – Hall of Justice   *Wagner, Grant, Mills and McMahon*   UK £4.50/US $7.95

Judge Dredd – Metal Fatigue   *Wagner, Grant, Bolland*   UK £4.50/US $7.95

D.R. & Quinch   *Alan Moore and Alan Davis*   UK £7.99/US $10.95

If you have any difficulty obtaining these books, you can order direct from:

Fleetway Books, Lazahold Ltd, PO Box 10, Roper Street, Pallion Industrial Estate, Sunderland SR4 6SN. Tel (091) 510 8787.

UK customers please send a cheque or postal order. For postage and packing, on orders up to £5 add £1.20; on orders up to £10 add £2; over £10 add £3.50.

Overseas (excluding USA) and Eire customers please send either a cheque drawn on a UK Bank, an International Money Order or Bankers Draft in Sterling. Postage and packing rates available on request.

All orders to be made payable to Maxwell Consumer Publishing and Communications Ltd. While every effort is made to keep prices steady, it is sometimes necessary to increase prices at short notice. Fleetway Books reserves the right to show on covers and charge new retail prices which may differ from those advertised here or elsewhere.

USA customers please send for a catalogue from SQP Inc, PO Box 4569, Toms River, New Jersey 08754.

*Not available in the USA